MAY

	Frank	Molly	Ben	
23 Monday	8.30 Give Blood / Working Late	TOOTHBRUSHES / Buy seeds / DENTIST 4:30	Take Sims to Jemal → / HUGE MATHS TEST!!	Birthday Presents for Grandad
24 Tuesday		GOVS meeting 8pm	Tennis / ~~Remember Jacintha Watson~~ / Becky after school	mum JAFFACAKES / cuttlefish
25 Wednesday	Phoe Stan Badminton 7.00	Finish book / Annual Review 3pm	BANDPRACTICE / Scout Subs / DRAMA CLUB	
26 Thursday	FINAL HOLIDAY DEPOSIT / Suit - Dry cleaners	Book Club Chloé's 8pm	JA's / earplugs! / Detention	Violin lesson 9:15am
27 Friday	GUTTERS! / Dinner with Boss £15.00 7.30	Lottie Key / Leaflets 7.30	English Essay / no chance! → Nick Ben's Walkman / sleepover at Sarah's	BIN BAGS!!! / Dishwasher Salt
28 Saturday	7.30 Jog with Debbie / UNITED 2.30 / Make Cake	Aromatherapy The Lab 3.00	Call Megs School MAC / Odeon 6.45 / Pocket money (don't forget mum!!) / Ha Ha Ben's got a girlfriend!	Wash P.E Kits
29 Sunday	DAD's 75th Royal Oak 12.15	Swimming		POND / → Cake!

THIS 2013 YEAR

JANUARY
M   7 14 21 28
T 1 8 15 22 29
W 2 9 16 23 30
T 3 10 17 24 31
F 4 11 18 25
S 5 12 19 26
S 6 13 20 27

FEBRUARY
M 4 11 18 25
T 5 12 19 26
W 6 13 20 27
T 7 14 21 28
F 1 8 15 22
S 2 9 16 23
S 3 10 17 24

MARCH
M 4 11 18 25
T 5 12 19 26
W 6 13 20 27
T 7 14 21 28
F 1 8 15 22 29
S 2 9 16 23 30
S 3 10 17 24 31

APRIL
M 1 8 15 22 29
T 2 9 16 23 30
W 3 10 17 24
T 4 11 18 25
F 5 12 19 26
S 6 13 20 27
S 7 14 21 28

MAY
M 6 13 20 27
T 7 14 21 28
W 1 8 15 22 29
T 2 9 16 23 30
F 3 10 17 24 31
S 4 11 18 25
S 5 12 19 26

JUNE
M 3 10 17 24
T 4 11 18 25
W 5 12 19 26
T 6 13 20 27
F 7 14 21 28
S 1 8 15 22 29
S 2 9 16 23 30

JULY
M 1 8 15 22 29
T 2 9 16 23 30
W 3 10 17 24 31
T 4 11 18 25
F 5 12 19 26
S 6 13 20 27
S 7 14 21 28

AUGUST
M 5 12 19 26
T 6 13 20 27
W 7 14 21 28
T 1 8 15 22 29
F 2 9 16 23 30
S 3 10 17 24 31
S 4 11 18 25

SEPTEMBER
M 2 9 16 23 30
T 3 10 17 24
W 4 11 18 25
T 5 12 19 26
F 6 13 20 27
S 7 14 21 28
S 1 8 15 22 29

OCTOBER
M 7 14 21 28
T 1 8 15 22 29
W 2 9 16 23 30
T 3 10 17 24 31
F 4 11 18 25
S 5 12 19 26
S 6 13 20 27

NOVEMBER
M 4 11 18 25
T 5 12 19 26
W 6 13 20 27
T 7 14 21 28
F 1 8 15 22 29
S 2 9 16 23 30
S 3 10 17 24

DECEMBER
M 2 9 16 23 30
T 3 10 17 24 31
W 4 11 18 25
T 5 12 19 26
F 6 13 20 27
S 7 14 21 28
S 1 8 15 22 29

The phases of the moon will be shown thus :—
● NEW MOON ☽ FIRST QUARTER ○ FULL MOON ☾ LAST QUARTER

NEXT 2014 YEAR

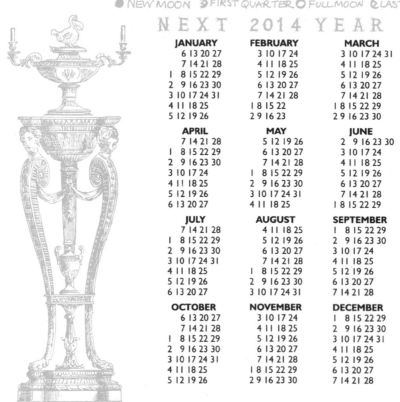

JANUARY
6 13 20 27
7 14 21 28
1 8 15 22 29
2 9 16 23 30
3 10 17 24 31
4 11 18 25
5 12 19 26

FEBRUARY
3 10 17 24
4 11 18 25
5 12 19 26
6 13 20 27
7 14 21 28
1 8 15 22
2 9 16 23

MARCH
3 10 17 24 31
4 11 18 25
5 12 19 26
6 13 20 27
7 14 21 28
1 8 15 22 29
2 9 16 23 30

APRIL
7 14 21 28
1 8 15 22 29
2 9 16 23 30
3 10 17 24
4 11 18 25
5 12 19 26
6 13 20 27

MAY
5 12 19 26
6 13 20 27
7 14 21 28
1 8 15 22 29
2 9 16 23 30
3 10 17 24 31
4 11 18 25

JUNE
2 9 16 23 30
3 10 17 24
4 11 18 25
5 12 19 26
6 13 20 27
7 14 21 28
1 8 15 22 29

JULY
7 14 21 28
1 8 15 22 29
2 9 16 23 30
3 10 17 24 31
4 11 18 25
5 12 19 26
6 13 20 27

AUGUST
4 11 18 25
5 12 19 26
6 13 20 27
7 14 21 28
1 8 15 22 29
2 9 16 23 30
3 10 17 24 31

SEPTEMBER
1 8 15 22 29
2 9 16 23 30
3 10 17 24
4 11 18 25
5 12 19 26
6 13 20 27
7 14 21 28

OCTOBER
6 13 20 27
7 14 21 28
1 8 15 22 29
2 9 16 23 30
3 10 17 24 31
4 11 18 25
5 12 19 26

NOVEMBER
3 10 17 24
4 11 18 25
5 12 19 26
6 13 20 27
7 14 21 28
1 8 15 22 29
2 9 16 23 30

DECEMBER
1 8 15 22 29
2 9 16 23 30
3 10 17 24 31
4 11 18 25
5 12 19 26
6 13 20 27
7 14 21 28

Published by Dodo Pad Ltd. PO Box 33, St. Agnes Cornwall TR5 0WU

Compilation & Original Illustration by Naomi McBride 2012

Illustrations © Dodo Pad Ltd 2012 © B M Peak 1995, 2012 © Rose Verney 1965, 2012

Dodo Pad Desk Diary – ISBN 978 0 857700 30 8 / DodoPAX loose-leaf Diary - ISBN 978 0 857700 33 9

Reprographics by Peta Bull Design.

Imprinted in China using paper sourced from sustainable forests.

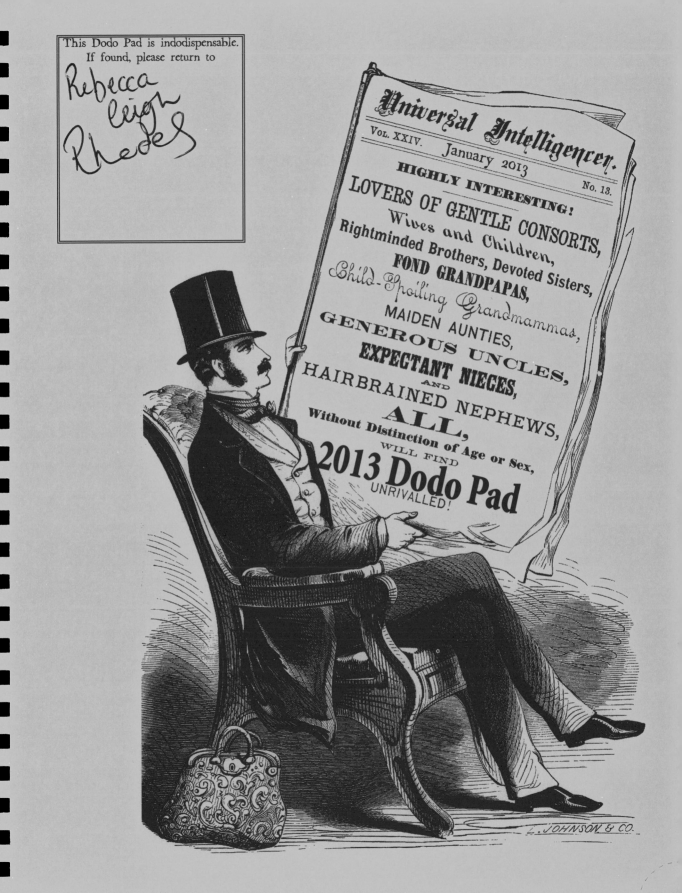

Universal Intelligencer.

Vol. XXIV. January 2013 No. 13.

HIGHLY INTERESTING!

LOVERS OF GENTLE CONSORTS,
Wives and Children,
Rightminded Brothers, Devoted Sisters,
FOND GRANDPAPAS,
Child-Spoiling Grandmammas,
MAIDEN AUNTIES,
GENEROUS UNCLES,
EXPECTANT NIECES,
AND
HAIRBRAINED NEPHEWS,
ALL,
Without Distinction of Age or Sex,
WILL FIND
2013 Dodo Pad
UNRIVALLED!

L. JOHNSON & CO.

HOW TO GET THE BEST
FROM YOUR DODO-PAD

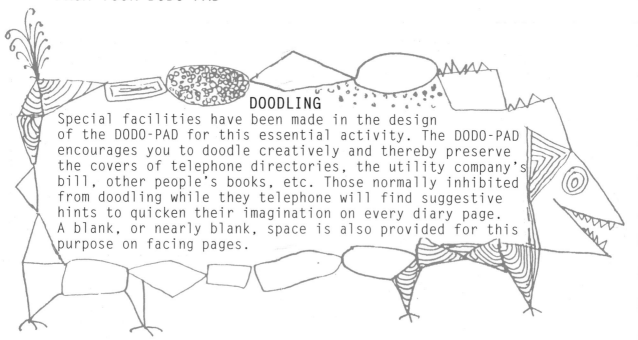

DOODLING

Special facilities have been made in the design
of the DODO-PAD for this essential activity. The DODO-PAD
encourages you to doodle creatively and thereby preserve
the covers of telephone directories, the utility company's
bill, other people's books, etc. Those normally inhibited
from doodling while they telephone will find suggestive
hints to quicken their imagination on every diary page.
A blank, or nearly blank, space is also provided for this
purpose on facing pages.

FURTHER USES FOR THE DODO PAD

Finished sheets can be torn out and are especially suitable
for making paper boats, darts, book-markers or tapers for
lighting a barbeque. If folded into eight, a DODO-PAD page
comes in handy for wedging up a rickety table or stuffing
onto a shaky sash-window. The most attractively doodled
pages make a personal type of Christmas card.

INSECTICIDE

The DODO-PAD makes an ideal weapon for swatting flies. Held
flat on the palm of the hand, it can also be used as a
missile against wasps and mosquitoes on the ceiling.

The DODO-PAD is so designed that it may be carried in
a shopping basket or kept chained to the telephone (for
instructions on how to chain your DODO-PAD to the telephone
see para. on opposite page).

A BURGLAR DISTRACTOR

"While he was giggling over my DODO-PAD I was able to get dressed and call the police" (name supplied).

DODO-PAD ALBUMS

If, at the end of a year, you wish to keep what amounts to a unique record of your, or your family's conscious and unconscious experience, we supply leather-bound folders with gold embossed lettering. Prices from £1069.50.

CHRISTMAS AND BIRTHDAYS

Extra pages are provided at the end to facilitate the systematic giving, or receipt, of presents. And for playing…

THE DODO-PAD GAME

Time can be pleasantly spent, while waiting for a Call Centre to answer, by imagining yourself as some well-known personality and filling in his or her engagements. But bear in mind the laws of libel, if your DODO-PAD is liable to be seen by others outside the family circle.

HOW TO CHAIN YOUR DODO-PAD TO THE TELEPHONE

Any reputable ironmonger will supply you with a length of thin chain. A DODO-PADLOCK can be obtained from us. Price £799.99, including postage.

DODO-PADDLERS ARE ADVISED TO ORDER THEIR NEXT YEAR'S DODO-PAD WELL IN ADVANCE TO BE SURE OF SAFE DELIVERY

2013

JANUARY 2013

1 T	NEW YEAR'S DAY	17 Th	
2 W		18 F	
3 Th		19 S	
4 F		20 Su	
5 S		21 M	MARTIN LUTHER KING DAY (US)
6 Su		22 T	
7 M		23 W	
8 T		24 Th	
9 W		25 F	BURNS' NIGHT
10 Th		26 S	
11 F		27 Su	
12 S		28 M	AUSTRALIA DAY (OBS)
13 Su		29 T	
14 M		30 W	
15 T		31 Th	
16 W			

FEBRUARY 2013

1 F		17 Su	
2 S		18 M	PRESIDENTS' DAY (US)
3 Su		19 T	
4 M		20 W	
5 T		21 Th	
6 W	WAITANGI DAY (NZ)	22 F	
7 Th		23 S	
8 F		24 Su	
9 S		25 M	
10 Su	CHINESE NEW YEAR	26 T	
11 M		27 W	
12 T	SHROVE TUESDAY	28 Th	
13 W			
14 Th			**Public Holidays et al.** This information is correct at time of going to press. The publishers accept no responsibility for any errors.
15 F			
16 S			

MARCH 2013

1 F		17 Su	ST PATRICK'S DAY (EIRE)
2 S		18 M	
3 Su		19 T	
4 M		20 W	
5 T		21 Th	
6 W		22 F	
7 Th		23 S	
8 F		24 Su	
9 S		25 M	
10 Su	MOTHER'S DAY (UK & EIRE)	26 T	PASSOVER
11 M	COMMONWEALTH DAY CANBERRA DAY	27 W	
12 T		28 Th	
13 W		29 F	GOOD FRIDAY
14 Th		30 S	
15 F		31 Su	EASTER DAY BST BEGINS
16 S			

APRIL 2013

1 M	EASTER MONDAY	17 W	
2 T		18 Th	
3 W		19 F	
4 Th		20 S	
5 F		21 Su	
6 S		22 M	
7 Su		23 T	
8 M		24 W	
9 T		25 Th	ANZAC DAY (AUS & NZ)
10 W		26 F	
11 Th		27 S	
12 F		28 Su	
13 S		29 M	
14 Su		30 T	
15 M			
16 T			

MAY 2013

1 W		17 F	
2 Th		18 S	
3 F		19 Su	
4 S		20 M	VICTORIA DAY (CANADA)
5 Su		21 T	
6 M	MAY BANK HOLIDAY (UK & EIRE)	22 W	
7 T		23 Th	
8 W		24 F	
9 Th		25 S	
10 F		26 Su	
11 S		27 M	SPRING BANK HOLIDAY (UK) MEMORIAL DAY (US)
12 Su	MOTHER'S DAY (US & AUS)	28 T	
13 M		29 W	
14 T		30 Th	
15 W		31 F	
16 Th			

JUNE 2013

1 S		17 M	
2 Su		18 T	
3 M	BANK HOLIDAY (EIRE)	19 W	
4 T		20 Th	
5 W		21 F	
6 Th		22 S	
7 F		23 Su	
8 S		24 M	
9 Su		25 T	
10 M		26 W	
11 T		27 Th	
12 W		28 F	
13 Th		29 S	
14 F		30 Su	
15 S			
16 Su	FATHER'S DAY (UK, US & CAN)		

JULY 2013

1 M	CANADA DAY	17 W	
2 T		18 Th	
3 W		19 F	
4 Th	INDEPENDENCE DAY (US)	20 S	
5 F		21 Su	
6 S		22 M	
7 Su		23 T	
8 M		24 W	
9 T	RAMADAN BEGINS	25 Th	
10 W		26 F	
11 Th		27 S	
12 F	PUBLIC HOLIDAY (N. IRELAND)	28 Su	
13 S		29 M	
14 Su	BASTILLE DAY	30 T	
15 M		31 W	
16 T			

AUGUST 2013

1 Th		17 S	
2 F		18 Su	
3 S		19 M	
4 Su		20 T	
5 M	SUMMER BANK HOLIDAY (SCOTLAND & EIRE)	21 W	
6 T		22 Th	
7 W		23 F	
8 Th		24 S	
9 F		25 Su	
10 S		26 M	SUMMER BANK HOLIDAY (UK)
11 Su		27 T	
12 M		28 W	
13 T		29 Th	
14 W		30 F	
15 Th		31 S	
16 F			

SEPTEMBER 2013

1 Su	FATHER'S DAY (AUS)	17 T	
2 M	LABOR DAY (US & CAN)	18 W	
3 T		19 Th	
4 W		20 F	
5 Th	ROSH HASHANAH	21 S	
6 F		22 Su	
7 S		23 M	
8 Su		24 T	
9 M		25 W	
10 T		26 Th	
11 W		27 F	
12 Th		28 S	
13 F		29 Su	
14 S	YOM KIPPUR	30 M	
15 Su			
16 M			

OCTOBER 2013

1 T		17 Th	
2 W		18 F	
3 Th		19 S	
4 F		20 Su	
5 S		21 M	
6 Su		22 T	
7 M		23 W	
8 T		24 Th	
9 W		25 F	
10 Th		26 S	
11 F		27 Su	BST ENDS
12 S		28 M	HOLIDAY (EIRE)
13 Su		29 T	
14 M	COLUMBUS DAY (US) THANKSGIVING (CANADA)	30 W	
15 T	EID AL-ADHA	31 Th	HALLOWE'EN
16 W			

NOVEMBER 2013

1 F		17 Su	
2 S		18 M	
3 Su	DIWALI	19 T	
4 M	MUSLIM NEW YEAR	20 W	
5 T	GUY FAWKES' NIGHT	21 Th	
6 W		22 F	
7 Th		23 S	
8 F		24 Su	
9 S		25 M	
10 Su	REMEMBRANCE SUNDAY (UK)	26 T	
11 M	VETERANS' DAY (US) REMEMBRANCE DAY (CAN)	27 W	
12 T		28 Th	THANKSGIVING (US) HANUKKAH
13 W		29 F	
14 Th		30 S	
15 F			
16 S			

DECEMBER 2013

1 Su		17 T	
2 M		18 W	
3 T		19 Th	
4 W		20 F	
5 Th		21 S	
6 F		22 Su	
7 S		23 M	
8 Su		24 T	
9 M		25 W	CHRISTMAS DAY
10 T		26 Th	BOXING DAY (UK, AUS, NZ) ST STEPHEN'S DAY (EIRE)
11 W		27 F	
12 Th		28 S	
13 F		29 Su	
14 S		30 M	
15 Su		31 T	
16 M			

December
2012

24 Monday

25 Tuesday

Christmas Day

26 Wednesday

Boxing Day UK, AUS, NZ

St Stephen's Day IRE

27 Thursday

28 Friday

29 Saturday

30 Sunday

Week 52

December 2012
January 2013

31 Monday

1 Tuesday

New Year's Day

2 Wednesday

Bank Holiday Scotland

3 Thursday

4 Friday

5 Saturday

6 Sunday

It is His Lordship's proud boast that Dodocorp leads the field in global publishing technology. However, in the privacy of his study he can sometimes be glimpsed clutching his battered old fountain pen, clicking on his abacus, a bakelite telephone clamped to his ear, while a wind-up gramophone plays softly but scratchily in the background. A nostalgic tear occasionally courses down one cheek. When young Viscount James Dodo burst in one day, disturbing his reverie, to show him this QR code, he at first took it to be a modern variation of his childhood favourite game of draughts, and was just dodusting off his old ivory chequerboard when young James put him right. Enthralled, he sent it straight down to the IT team at Canadodo Towers (by native bearer and cleft stick) who have honed and developed it for a special surprise prize in this year's Dodo Pad. You will need to dodecipher the code above to learn more...

Sam Spade, Mr Hammett's über-tough detective hero, was used to receiving threats and cryptic notes, working as he did on the seedier side of the tracks. However this anonymous letter not only tested his analytical skills but also his lingual dexterity.   Try reading it out loud – quickly!

JANUARY 2013

7 Monday

8 Tuesday

9 Wednesday

10 Thursday

11 Friday

1961 Death of crime writer Dashiell Hammett, author of 'The Maltese Falcon'

●

12 Saturday

13 Sunday

My Birthday ♡

Scan me to win a
competition!

'MALICE IN WONDERLAND'
Jean Cocteau's description of Cecil Beaton

January 2013

14 Monday — 1904 Birth of Cecil Beaton, society photographer and designer

15 Tuesday

16 Wednesday

17 Thursday

18 Friday

19 Saturday

20 Sunday

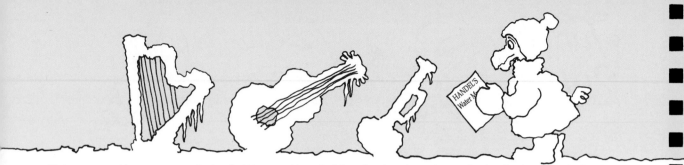

This year the very original Vienna Vegetable Orchestra (see Dodo Pads passim) plan to travel to Gielo, where the Ice Music Festival is held, to collaborate on a new work, a Symphony of Frozen Vegetables. Birds Eye are the main sponsors of the event.

JANuary

2013

21 Monday

Martin Luther King Day US

22 Tuesday

23 Wednesday

24 Thursday

25 Friday

Burns' Night

26 Saturday

27 Sunday

Week 04

Norwegian Ice Music Festival begins in Gielo, traditionally at the first full moon of the year ◯

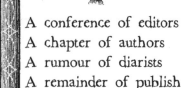

A conference of editors
A chapter of authors
A rumour of diarists
A remainder of publishers
A parthenon of columnists
A shorthand of journalists
A percentage of agents

The usual reward for
any other collective
nouns, pertinent to the
literary world, sent in by
Dodopadlers, which tickle
His Lordship's fancy

Scan this to dodiscover the lyrical #Twittale written by His Lordship's loyal
dodopadlers. There's a reward for the most intriguing first line for the next
one (in 120 characters or less) to arrive by 28/02/13 @lord_dodo #Twittale

January February

2013

28 Monday

Australia Day (obs)

29 Tuesday

30 Wednesday

31 Thursday

Feast Day of St John Bosco, patron saint of, amongst others, editors

1 Friday

2 Saturday

3 Sunday

The winning doodle of last year's adult National Doodle Day competition, by Carl Wildon

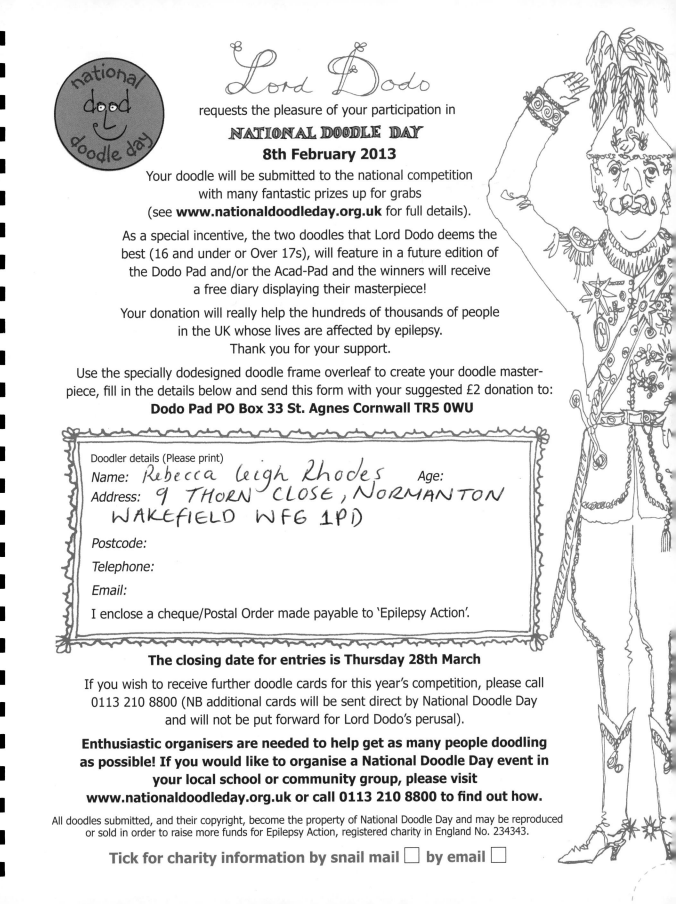

national doodle day

Lord Dodo

requests the pleasure of your participation in

NATIONAL DOODLE DAY
8th February 2013

Your doodle will be submitted to the national competition
with many fantastic prizes up for grabs
(see **www.nationaldoodleday.org.uk** for full details).

As a special incentive, the two doodles that Lord Dodo deems the
best (16 and under or Over 17s), will feature in a future edition of
the Dodo Pad and/or the Acad-Pad and the winners will receive
a free diary displaying their masterpiece!

Your donation will really help the hundreds of thousands of people
in the UK whose lives are affected by epilepsy.
Thank you for your support.

Use the specially dodesigned doodle frame overleaf to create your doodle masterpiece, fill in the details below and send this form with your suggested £2 donation to:
Dodo Pad PO Box 33 St. Agnes Cornwall TR5 0WU

Doodler details (Please print)

Name: *Rebecca Leigh Rhodes*   Age:

Address: 9 THORN CLOSE, NORMANTON
WAKEFIELD WF6 1PD

Postcode:

Telephone:

Email:

I enclose a cheque/Postal Order made payable to 'Epilepsy Action'.

The closing date for entries is Thursday 28th March

If you wish to receive further doodle cards for this year's competition, please call
0113 210 8800 (NB additional cards will be sent direct by National Doodle Day
and will not be put forward for Lord Dodo's perusal).

**Enthusiastic organisers are needed to help get as many people doodling
as possible! If you would like to organise a National Doodle Day event in
your local school or community group, please visit
www.nationaldoodleday.org.uk or call 0113 210 8800 to find out how.**

Tick for charity information by snail mail ☐ by email ☐

FEBRUARY 2013

Week 06

4 MONDAY

5 TUESDAY

6 WEDNESDAY

Waitangi Day NZ

7 THURSDAY

8 FRIDAY

NATIONAL ·· DOODLE ···· DAY !

9 SATURDAY

10 SUNDAY

Chinese New Year

St. Valentine's Day

February 2013

11 Monday

12 Tuesday

Shrove Tuesday

13 Wednesday

14 Thursday

Valentine's Day

15 Friday

16 Saturday

17 Sunday

Louis Roederer CHAMPAGNE

That **money** talks,
I'll not deny.
I heard it **once**, it said
'Goodbye!'.
Richard Armour

February 2013

18 Monday

19 Tuesday

20 Wednesday

21 Thursday

22 Friday

23 Saturday

24 Sunday

Week 08

Presidents' Day US

1822 Death of Thomas Coutts, founder of the eponymous bank

The music **teacher**
came in **twice a week**
to **bridge**
the **awful gap**
between **Dorothy**
and **Chopin**
George Ade 1866-1944

25 Monday

26 Tuesday

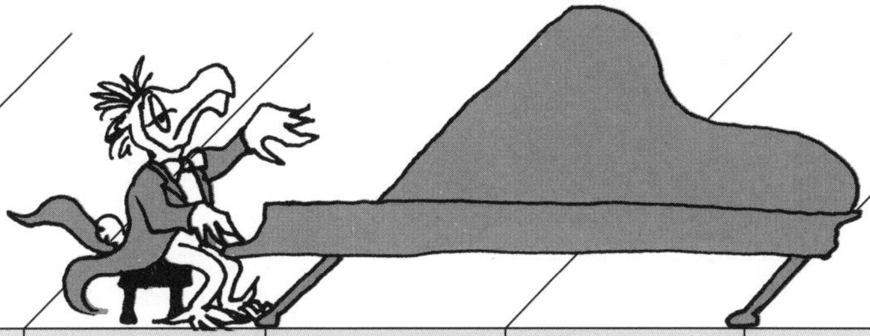

27 Wednesday

28 Thursday

1 Friday

2 Saturday

3 Sunday

Week 09

1810 Birth of Frédéric Chopin

St David's Day

"Yes, one does want to make one's Mummy just as nice as possible". James McNeill Whistler, on being complimented on the portrait of his mother.

March
2013

4 Monday

5 Tuesday

6 Wednesday

7 Thursday

8 Friday

9 Saturday

10 Sunday

Week 10

Mother's Day UK & IRE

'I want to be a lawn'

Serious gardeners need a good sense of HUMUS

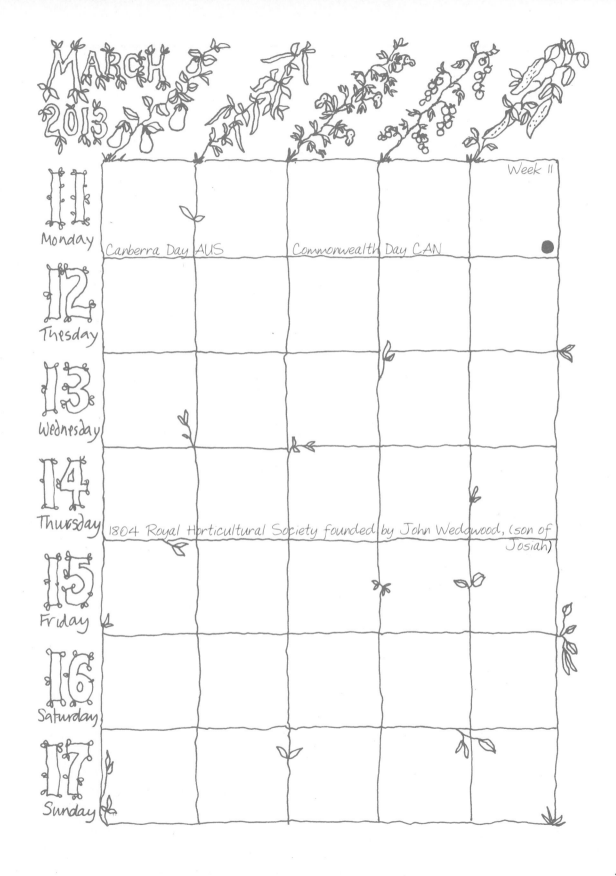

MARCH 2013

Week 11

11 Monday

Canberra Day AUS Commonwealth Day CAN

12 Tuesday

13 Wednesday

14 Thursday

1804 Royal Horticultural Society founded by John Wedgwood, (son of Josiah)

15 Friday

16 Saturday

17 Sunday

His Lordship and his Head Gardener make the unwelcome discovery that young Master Ludodo, a keen if some what dyslexic horticulturalist, has been mixing up the cabbage seed and the birdseed again.

MARCH 2013

	18 MONDAY				

18 MONDAY

19 TUESDAY

20 WEDNESDAY

1917 Birth of Dame Vera Lynn

21 THURSDAY

22 FRIDAY

23 SATURDAY

24 SUNDAY

I'm pink
therefore I'm
spam

Grafitti spotted in
the Philosophy Department
of Cambridge University

March 2013

Columns: Work | [horse] | mche | Family life *

Week 13

Date	Work		mche	Family life *
25 Monday				
26 Tuesday				
27 Wednesday	Passover			○
28 Thursday				
29 Friday	12hrs Cedar / Good Friday			Paul. Catherine gift
30 Saturday	Weekend off with moo / Easter Day	Meal at the Ship	Couldn't get eggs :(	Get bag back from mum	Party Wingfield — Get flowers
31 Sunday			1596 Birth of	René Descartes	BST begins / Clocks Back

* Descartes before the horse

* Tuesday 2nd Long Day - April
Wednesday 27th March LD
Thursday 28th March LD
Friday 29th March LD
*
Wednesday 3rd April - Training
Thursday 4th April - Training
Saturday 6th April - LD
Sunday 7th April - LD

Overtime
Monday 8th
OR
Tuesday 9th

Wednesday 17th
Thursday 18th

*Woody Allen, from The Book of Isaiah, quoted in
'Peaceable Kingdom' by Edward Hicks*

APRIL 2013

	Work	Home		Family	
1 Monday	Shift Swap with mum *Easter Monday*	Day off with mike		Call mum	
2 Tuesday	12hrs Cedar N/S				Paid John for lift
3 Wednesday	Mapa training 09:30 - 16:30	Pay Rent ✓	Shopping @ 18:05 Asda		ᗺ
4 Thursday	2nd Day Mapa training 09:30 - 16:30			Show helen pics for claim	Get annual leave form
5 Friday	Day Off	START Gathering Holiday Items up	Meet Mike in LEEDS ♥	Call MUM about Driving	
6 Saturday	12hr shift Cedar			Ask mum about lift	
7 Sunday	12hr shift Cedar			Ask mum about lift to work	

1780 Birth of Edward Hicks, American 'primitive' painter of allegorical scenes

The rabbit has a charming face; its private life is a disgrace

I really dare not name to you the awful things that rabbits do

Anon

APRIL 2013

	Work	Home	Mike	Family	Remember to:
8 Monday	Day off (Swap round)				
9 Tuesday	Hospital finish 14:00	Put washing in	Make Mike Dinner	Gran in Hospital	Call mum about Gran
10 Wednesday	Long Day Shift	look online for uni-courses			Take Payment form in for Helen
11 Thursday	Long Day Shift	Ask Funke for new annual leave sheet.			Pay uncle John for lifts
12 Friday	Long Day Shift				Call about classes → tell charlie
13 Saturday	Off Work	Get holiday stuff together	Buy Mike's present and card.	Go driving with Dad	Borrow money from mum for day out
14 Sunday	Off Work	Becca and Mike anniversary		Go driving with day out	for a meal

1926 Birth of Hugh Hefner, creator of the Playboy Empire

Weekend Off?

WHILE PREPARING SOME OF HIS TROOPS FOR BATTLE, FEWER THAN 500 IN TOTAL, AGAMEMNON WAS HAVING TROUBLE GETTING THEM INTO EVEN ROWS FOR PARADE. HE LINED THEM UP IN THREES, BUT THERE WAS ONE LEFT OVER. THEN HE TRIED ROWS OF FOUR, FIVE AND SIX - SAME PROBLEM. LUCKILY ODYSSEUS, ALWAYS THE WISE COUNSELLOR, WAS ABLE TO ADVISE HIM BEFORE TROUBLE BREWED, AND WHEN HE PUT THEM IN ROWS OF SEVEN, THE ROWS WERE EXACTLY EVEN. HOW MANY SOLDIERS WERE LINED UP ON PARADE?

Get helen's phone number
Get annual leave sheet

ANSWER IN THE APPENDIX

APRIL 2013

Work/home | Home | Family

Woohoo! 9 weeks till Hols

	Work		Home	Family	
15 MONDAY	Long Day Shift Cedar		Put. Washing on.	Mum lent £100	
16 TUESDAY	Long Day Shift		Tidy house after work	mum lift home	
17 WEDNESDAY	Overtime Shift – 17:00hrs then meetings	moo! moo.	Make sure funding closes AL sheet		NEED TO pay C.N for lifts
18 THURSDAY	Overtime Shift 8-2 Cedar	Put mike's dinner on!	Clean House when finnish.	Sort out driving lessons	∋
19 FRIDAY	Training 09:30 – 16:30				
20 SATURDAY					
21 SUNDAY	Cut off day for wages long Day shift				

1178BC Return of Odysseus to Ithaca after 10 years *

* A team of scientists have recently dodeduced this exact date
by studying astronomical events mentioned in The Odyssey

Start sunbed sessions on Saturday;

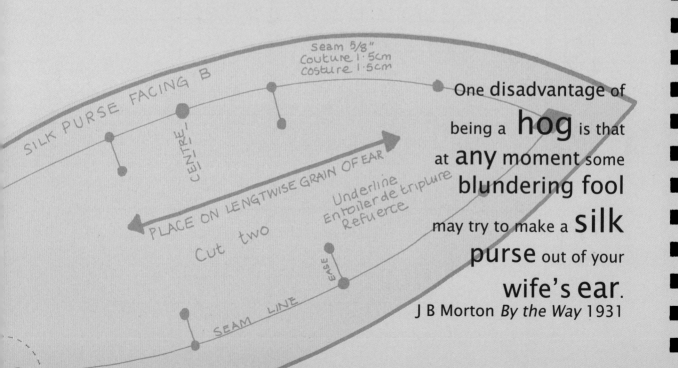

SILK PURSE FACING B

Seam 5/8"
Couture 1·5cm
costure 1·5cm

CENTRE

PLACE ON LENGTWISE GRAIN OF EAR

Underline
Entoiler de tripure
Refuerce

Cut two

EASE

SEAM LINE

One disadvantage of
being a **hog** is that
at **any** moment some
blundering fool
may try to make a **silk**
purse out of your
wife's ear.
J B Morton *By the Way* 1931

APRIL
2013

Week 17

22 Monday

23 Tuesday

St George's Day

24 Wednesday

25 Thursday

ANZAC Day

26 Friday

Pay Day!

1989 Revival of traditional Pig Race in Naas, Co. Kildare, Ireland

27 Saturday

28 Sunday

8 week

A journalist from the Leinster Leader told His Lordship, a keen racing-pig breeder, that the race winner was Harry Trotter, who beat off stiff competition from Sir Oinksalot, Porky's Revenge, Cheeky Chops and Brown Sauce.

DODUbIOUS INFORMATION

Mauritius is the first recorded centre of greyhound racing, and at the Champs de Mars, the premier racing venue in on the island, it is customary to use a mechanical dodo to entice the greyhounds round the track. Use of the genuine article was the true cause of the species' demise.

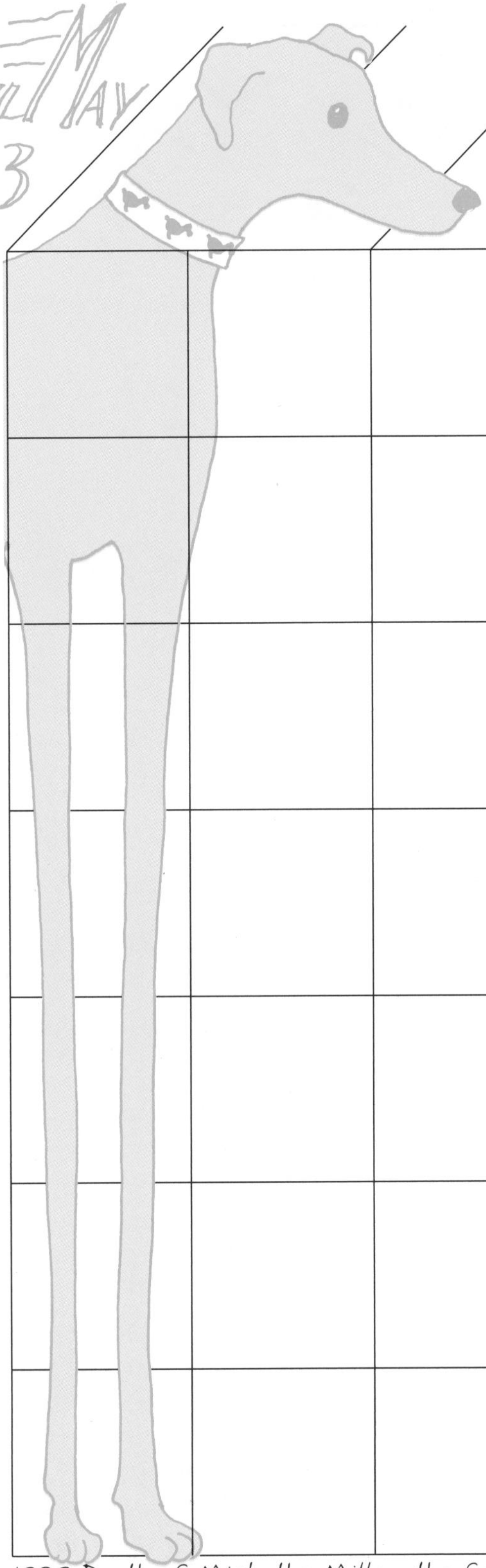

Week 18

29 MONDAY

30 TUESDAY

1 WEDNESDAY

2 THURSDAY

3 FRIDAY

4 SATURDAY

5 SUNDAY

1939 Death of Mick the Miller, the first star of greyhound racing.
He was bred by Fr Martin Brophy in County Offaly, Ireland

Just because swans mate for life,
I don't think it's that big a deal.
First of all, if you're a swan,
you're probably not going to find
a swan that looks much better
than the one you've got, so why
not mate for life?

Jack Handy

May

2013

Week 19

6 Monday

Spring Bank Holiday UK

7 Tuesday

1840 Birth of Pyotr Ilyich Tchaikovsky

8 Wednesday

9 Thursday

10 Friday

11 Saturday

12 Sunday

Mother's Day US & AUS

* Put myself down for
overtime.

Scan me to win a
competition!

In view of the troubled
times we live in, the
Cats' Protection League
now offer a full Close
Purrsonal Bodyguard
Service.

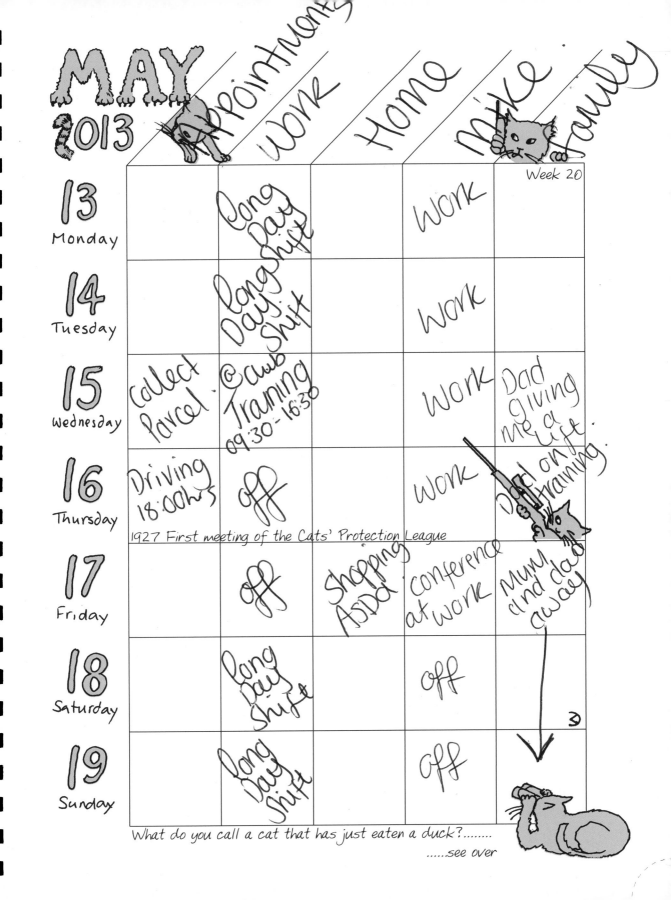

MAY 2013

	Appointments	Work	Home	Mike	Family
					Week 20
13 Monday		Long Day Shift		Work	
14 Tuesday		Long Day. Shift		Work	
15 Wednesday	Collect Parcel.	@ club Training 09:30 - 16:30		Work	Dad giving me a lift
16 Thursday	Driving 18:00hrs	Off		Work	Dad on Training
1927 First meeting of the Cats' Protection League					
17 Friday		Off	Shopping ASDA	Conference at work	Mum and dad away
18 Saturday		Long Day Shift		Off	③
19 Sunday		Long Day Shift		Off	

What do you call a cat that has just eaten a duck?.........

.......see over

If it ain't Baroque, don't fix it

...a duck-filled fattypuss

MAY 2013

	Appointments	Work	Home	Mike	Family
20 Monday	Victoria Day CAN	Overtime? long Day Maple 8-8			Week 21
21 Tuesday	Driving Lesson 18:00 hrs from Home	Overtime 8-16:30 Cedar 10U			Mum giving Me lift home.
22 Wednesday		long Day Shift — Off 10U			Call dad and let him know about van.
23 Thursday		long.Day Shift — Off 10U			
24 Friday	Organise a van for removal	Annual leave Shift	Pack all Stuff up	Get mike to start Packing up.	Call dad about moving van etc.
25 Saturday	Getting keys at 10:30 Reeds Rains	Off	Moving Day		Borrowing money from mum £550
26 Sunday		Off Cut off day.			Uncle Niel's 50th Birthday Party.

Doctors appointment 15:00 hrs ←

Feast Day of St Philip of Neri, whose canonisation in 1622, along with many other counter-reformation leaders including St Teresa of Avila, heralded the start of the Baroque style

Packing

* All cleaning products
* All plates, cups and crockery
* All food and drinks
* Hoover and mop + brush.

ещё dodubrous информация!

Lord Dodo's great–great uncle Vladimr Dodov owned vast forested estates north of St Petersburg, wood from which fed the papermills of His Lordship's publishing empire in pre–revolutionary times. In fact, Prince Dodov was himself a paper baron, publishing the avidly–read Ododessa edition of the *Gubernski Vedomost*. To celebrate his first million roubles' profit, the Prince commissioned M. Fabergé to fashion the stupendous creation drawn here. Sadly only this preparatory sketch survives – the beautiful egg was flattened to a pancake by the Bolsheviks, who knew no batter.

MAY JUNE 2013

	Appointments	Work	Home	mike	Family
27 Monday	Rent due on thorne close	Long Day Shift — Annual Leave shift	moving and cleaning new house		Week 22 Driving Lesson 14:00 -15:00
	Spring Bank Holiday UK				
28 Tuesday		Long Day Shift — IOU →	Spoke to Helen.		
29 Wednesday		Overtime? Cleaning house and packing	Sort out stuff and pack		
30 Thursday		Overtime? Off Try and IOU call Helen.D again			
	1846 Birth of Pyotr Karl Faberge				
31 Friday		Pay Day	Pay rent on thornes Close. £££		Ask dad to go Driving
1 Saturday	Sick at work	long Day IOU Shift			
2 Sunday		long Day IOU Shift			

'Oh!
I
h a v e
passed   a
miserable night', I may as well say,
as a greater man said before me.
The Irish Flea Association
were so occupied in holding a
session on human Physiology
upon my devoted body that
it was out of the question
to think of sleeping while
transactions   of   such
interest   were   going
forward. Early in the
morning I assassinated
4 of the committee
together with their
President,
Mr Bug.
Barclay Fox
1835

June 2013

	Appointments	Work	Home	Misc	Family
3 Monday		Overtime?			Week 23
	1924 Death of Franz Kafka			Queen's Birthday NZ	
4 Tuesday		Overtime?			
5 Wednesday		long Day Shift			
6 Thursday		long Day Shift			
7 Friday		long Day Shift			
8 Saturday		off			
9 Sunday		Off			

Lord Dodo's great-great grandfather used to keep a small private zoo in the grounds of Dodo Towers. Each April Fool's Day, to amuse the family, he issued instructions for keepers and animals to swap places. This went down very well for a few years, but things got out of hand when a well-dressed Nile crocodile locked his jaws on the the antelope keeper and, despite everyone's best efforts, refused to give him up. Reluctantly, Lord Dodo had to abandon this annual amusement soon afterwards, lamenting the cowardice of his keepers and the unsporting behaviour of the croc.

June 2013

	Appointments	Work	Home	Work lifts	family
10 Monday	Queen's Birthday AUS	Long Day Shift		John. morning mum Evening	Week 24
11 Tuesday	Call Reed's Rains — 1793 Jardin des Plantes, the first public zoo, opens in Paris	Long Day Shift		John. morning	
12 Wednesday		Overtime? 8-2 Cedar 2-8 larch		John. morning	
13 Thursday		~~overtime?~~ Shift Swap Sunday 8 - 8		John. morning	
14 Friday		Shift Swap Saturday 8 - 8		John morning	Buy Dad's father's day Present.
15 Saturday	G.	~~Long Day Shift~~			
16 Sunday	Driving Lesson 13:30 1hr — Father's Day UK, US, CAN	~~Long Day Shift~~	Pack up Stuff.	Go to Church with Charlie	father Day

Lord Dodo has long admired Mr Spencer's weekly Guardian column on vegetarian food, but when introduced to him at the Food Writers' Awards Ceremony, His Lordship was intrigued to learn of his prodigious, but less-well known, output in other genres. His plays include Romaine and Julienne, and A Sweet Potato Named Desirée; there's a biography of Lawrence of Arugula, and his novels, of sweeping breadth and power, include War and Peas, The Adventures of Huckleberry Fennel, Of Cumin Bondage and Lord of the Onion Rings. As Patron of the Viennese Vegetable Orchestra, Lord Dodo immediately commissioned a libretto from Mr Spencer for their forthcoming opera, Madame Butterbean.

Book Beauty appointments for Saturday; @ 09:30 am .

Nails.
Waxing

Organise move .
 - van
 - Getting keys @ 11:00 am .
 - Get metre readings
 - hand in keys at Richard kendall .
 - Clean house, Thornes close .
 - re-arrange beauty appointment .

Holiday - Organise lift to airport . 00:00 Dad .
 - Pack clothes / Suitcases .

June
2013

	Appointments	Work	Home	Mike	Family
17 Monday		~~overtime~~			Week 25 look after mum
18 Tuesday		~~overtime~~			look after mum.
19 Wednesday		long Day shift			
20 Thursday		long Day shift			
21 Friday		long Day shift ~~~~ Get shift swap!			
22 Saturday	09:30 hrs Beach hut appointment	off	lip wax ½ leg wax Bikini wax Eyebrow wax toe nails minxed		
23 Sunday		off			○

START OF ANNUAL LEAVE

Sun cream
Bug spray
Plug adapters
Bite Clicker
After Sun cream
Beach bag
towel x 2 for beach
Shampoo
conditioner.
GHDs / hair dryer
makeup / remover / flannel
Prickly heat cream
Prickly heat spray
Hair brush
tooth brushes
tooth paste.
Detangle hair brush
Hair spray
Wet wipes
Pill
Paracetamols / Ibruplofen

Nail polish
Body / shower gel
Small beach bag.
kindle
laptop.

Big Chief Dodo he say 2014 Dodo Pad on sale now
www.dodopad.com

{
Passports
tickets
transfers
Insurance
Travel money
}

June 2013

	Appointments	Work	Holiday	Mike	family
24 monday	Holiday flight @ 06:35	Annual leave Shift			lift to Airport from Dac).
25 tuesday		Annual leave Shift			
1876 Battle of Little Bighorn begins					
26 wednesday					
27 thursday					
28 friday		Pay Day!			
29 saturday		Annual leave Shift			
30 sunday		Annual leave Shift			

* Horse riding - €50
* Animal park - €24
* Catalanza - €55

MORE DODUBIOUS INFORMATION

This may come as a surprise to those Dodopadlers not acquainted with Las Vegas, but there are more Catholic churches than casinos in that brash and secular-seeming desert city.....

Not surprisingly, some worshippers at Sunday services give casino chips rather than cash when the collection is taken. Since they get chips from many different casinos, the churches have devised a method to collect the offerings.

The churches send all their collected chips to a nearby Redodemptorist Monastery for sorting, and then the chips are taken to the casinos of origin and cashed in.

This is done by the chip monks.

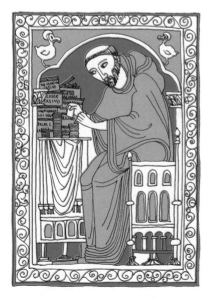

JULY
2013

DODO'S PALACE 24 HOUR CASINO

Week 27

1 MONDAY — Canada Day

2 TUESDAY

3 WEDNESDAY

4 THURSDAY — Independence Day US

5 FRIDAY

6 SATURDAY

7 SUNDAY — 1875 Joseph Jagger became the first person to break the bank at Monte Carlo

* Cole Porter

JULY 2013

8 Monday

9 Tuesday

Ramadan begins

10 Wednesday

11 Thursday

12 Friday

Holiday N. Ireland

13 Saturday

14 Sunday

1916 Hugo Ball recited the first Dada manifesto in Zurich

Week 28

Little Miss Dodo's Histery Lesson

Witch hunts erupted in countries such as Germany, England, Scotland and Salem. The victims were usually older post-marsupial women.

15
Monday

16
Tuesday

17
Wednesday

18
Thursday

19
Friday

20
Saturday

21
Sunday

Week 29

1692 First public hanging of some of the Salem 'witches'

YOU CAN ALWAYS TELL A HAPPY CYCLIST BY THE FLIES ON HIS TEETH

July 2013

22 Monday

○

23 Tuesday

24 Wednesday

2005 Lance Armstrong announces his (first) retirement from competitive cycling

25 Thursday

26 Friday

27 Saturday

28 Sunday

Scan me to win a competition!

On his return from a school cricketing trip to Mauritius, young Viscount James Dodo told his papa of the novel use to which the local team had put the complimentary Dodo Pads given out to each player. Always keen to expand the market for his products, Lord Dodo is now in negotiation with Lillywhites, hoping to supply the England side for the next World Cup.

There's been a colour clash - both teams are wearing white!
John Motson

JULY AUGUST 2013

29 Monday

30 Tuesday

31 Wednesday

Thursday

1990 Graham Gooch completed record innings of 456 runs in 1st Test Match against India at Lords

2 Friday

3 Saturday

4 Sunday

Lord Dodo acknowledges Beecham's Powders' claim to the first advertising slogan, but points out that Dodocorp has, from its foundation, employed some very sophisticated sales and marketing techniques. Here's a treasure he unearthed from the archive in a dodusty corner of the library at Dodo Towers, which gives Mr Beecham a run for his money.

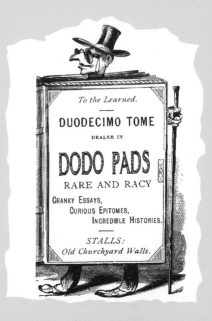

To the Learned.

DUODECIMO TOME

DEALER IN

DODO PADS

RARE AND RACY

CRANKY ESSAYS,
CURIOUS EPITOMES,
INCREDIBLE HISTORIES.

STALLS:
Old Churchyard Walls.

AUGUST
2013

Week 32

5 Monday

Bank Holiday Scotland & IRE

6 Tuesday

7 Wednesday

1859 'Worth a Guinea a Box' – the first known advertising slogan, on Beecham's Powders

8 Thursday

9 Friday

10 Saturday

11 Sunday

Planning this year's trip to the dodelightful Just So Festival, Lord Dodo was reminded of an engraving in the Dodo Towers Library, of great-great-great uncle "Spiro" Dodo at the Massacre of Chios in 1822, whose calm demeanour in moments of crisis was, by family repute, the inspiration for Mr Kipling's famous poem.

IF you can keep your head when all about you are losing theirs, it's just possible you haven't grasped the situation.
Jean Kerr

Week 33

12
Monday

13
Tuesday

14
Wednesday

15
Thursday

16
Friday

17
Saturday

18
Sunday

Just So Festival begins! *

*for more information go to www.justsofestival.org.uk

August
2013

19 Monday

20 Tuesday

21 Wednesday

22 Thursday

23 Friday

24 Saturday

25 Sunday

Week 34

1806 Death of Jean-Honoré Fragonard

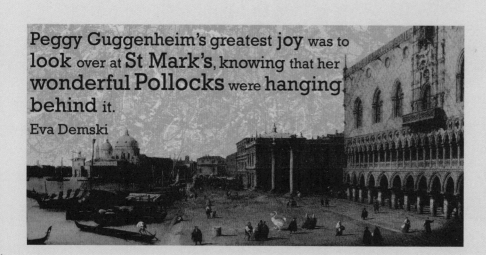

Peggy Guggenheim's greatest joy was to look over at St Mark's, knowing that her wonderful Pollocks were hanging behind it.

Eva Demski

AUGUST
SEPTEMBER
2013

GUGGENHEIM MUSEUM
NEW ACQUISITION

Week 35

26
Monday

Summer Bank Holiday UK (except Scotland)

1898 Birth of Peggy Guggenheim

27
Tuesday

28
Wednesday

ε

29
Thursday

30
Friday

31
Saturday

1
Sunday

Father's Day AUS

STORM IN A D CUP.. . . .

The bosom can be passing fair
That apes the apple or the pear:
I do not itch to lay my head
On melons or on loaves of bread
AP Herbert

September 2013

2 Monday

3 Tuesday

4 Wednesday

5 Thursday

6 Friday

7 Saturday

8 Sunday

Week 36

Labor Day US & CAN

Rosh Hashanah

1968 Bra-burning feminist protest at the Miss America Pageant

The Dodo family are terrible chatterboxes, which tries his Lordship's patience sorely from time to time. He encourages them to regularly attend a local support group for compulsive talkers – On Anon Anon.

Week 37

9 Monday

10 Tuesday

1855 Birth of archaeologist Robert Koldewey, discoverer of ancient Babylon and the foundations of the Tower of Babel

11 Wednesday

12 Thursday

13 Friday

14 Saturday

Yom Kippur

15 Sunday

LORD DODO INVITES YOU TO VISIT HIS STATELY PILE IN CYBERSPACE

NDD just used to mean 'New Dodo Development' but it now aptly shares its acronym with 'National Doodle Day', the charity which we proudly support each year - see page preceding 4th February for more details and please enter next year's competition!

Lord Dodo presents here a few products from his most marvellous range, but urges you to browse his highly informative website in order to avail yourself of the ever increasing selection of low tech answers to organising the high tech lifestyle.

So please, meander through his home and dodiscover his outstanding array of organisers and gift ideas, as well as a few surprises along the way...

LIMITED EDITION
LUXURIOUS ITALIAN LEATHER SLIPCOVERS

Each year, a brand new, collection of supple natural hide or silky smooth recycled leathers.

Notwithstanding why anyone might wish to hide their Dodo Pad or Acad-Pad, Lord Dodo has bowed to pressure and acknowledged the many requests for a handsome way of secreting or protecting the Dodo Pad's brightness and unbridled humour with a luxurious outer casing that should last for years and years.

Blind embossed with a subtle Dodo-Pad logo on the front cover and an elastic bandeau closure, choose from a selection of colours in natural hide or recycled leather.

These beautiful handmade Italian leather slipcovers are also available for the Mini Dodo Pad and Mini Acad-Pad.

We've also **Faux leather slipcovers** - just as gorgeous but more economical to buy!

Visit **www.dodopad.com**, call +44 (0)845 053 1166 or post your order to:
Dodo Pad, PO Box 33, St. Agnes, Cornwall TR5 0WU

LORD DODO'S DODETACHABLE ORDER FORM

Use this specially designed Dodorder Form if you prefer to order offline through the post or on the phone: 0845 053 1166. Lord Dodo's team is generally available from 9.00am – 5.30pm weekdays.

Name (please PRINT)

Address

Postcode/Zip

Tel No (in case of query) Day

Email

Delivery address (if different)

Evening

Code	Description	Qty	Unit Price £	Total
DDP14	2014 Dodo Pad Original Desk Diary (Spiral Bound)		12.95	
DWP14	2014 Dodo Wall Pad Calendar		12.95	
DDPM14	2014 Mini Dodo Pad		8.95	
DDPX14	2014 Dodo Pad PAX© version (NB. LOOSE LEAF FORMAT)		11.95	
DFXA14	2014 FiloFAX compatible A5 (148 X 210mm) diary insert		11.95	
DFXP14	2014 FiloFAX compatible Pers Org. (95 x 171mm) diary insert		10.95	
DFXL14	2014 A4/US Letter UNIVERSAL FiloFAX compatible loose leaf insert		14.95	
	Order Handling Charge (Please see website or catalogue for details)		£2.50	
	*Please see below for 'Low Order Value' and Overseas Postage Supplements**			
			Grand Total	£

*Low Order Value Supplement: If the total value of goods is less than £8.75 a single £2.95 supplement is payable.
Overseas Postage Supplements: For European delivery please add £2.25 for each £10 spent on goods; for World-Wide delivery add £3.25 for each £10 spent on goods.

I enclose a crossed cheque/PO payable to Dodo Pad Ltd or please debit my Visa/MasterCard/Amex/Maestro Card

Start date

Expiry date   Issue No. (if shown)   3 Digit Security Code

Signature   Date

USA and overseas orders: If you are paying with a non-UK credit card, your account will be debited with the UK sterling equivalent at the time of order processing.

You may order from Lord Dodo in any of the following ways:
Visit www.dodopad.com and order securely online
Mail Order hotline: +44 (0)845 053 1166 (local call rate)
Fax: +44 (0)845 634 6273 (local call rate)
Post: The Dodo Pad, PO Box 33, St. Agnes Cornwall TR5 0WU

code 13R

We aim to dispatch within 2 working days of receipt of your order but please allow up to 21 days for delivery, especially for international deliveries. Subject to availability. Prices shown here are correct at time of going to press.

Data Protection Act 1998 Lord Dodo would like to contact you from time to time to tell you of his new products and not-to-be-missed promotions. If you do not wish to receive these communications, please tick this box. ☐ Lord Dodo may, very occasionally, allow carefully screened organisations to contact his customers. If you do not wish to receive these communications, please tick this box. ☐ Opt out is available at any stage. Dodo Pad Ltd. is a registered data controller.

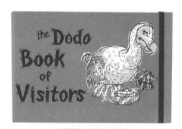
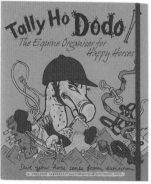

Prices are subject to change; those shown here are correct at time of going to press.

WELL £18.95
10% of the net price is donated to
the Wellbeing of Women charity

DBC £18.95

DCH £16.95
Paper refill DCHP £3.25
Card list x 5 DCHL5 £3.25
Card list x 10 DCHL10 £5.00

DTL £16.95

Visit dodopad.com for our complete range of full year,
mid year and filofax compatible diaries/calendars /refills

PWP £11.95

HSB £18.95

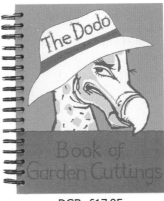

DGB £17.95

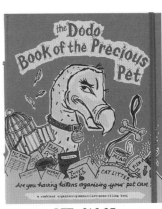

PET £16.95

Never incur the wrath of the moth
especially if you're a man of the cloth. *Anon*

September 2013

16 Monday

17 Tuesday

18 Wednesday

19 Thursday
1759 Birth of William Kirby, parson and entomologist

20 Friday

21 Saturday

22 Sunday

STAN'S HOUR

Why isn't phonetic spelt the way it sounds?

SEPT EMBER 2013

23 Monday

24 Tuesday

1896 Birth of F Scott Fitzgerald

25 Wednesday

26 Thursday

27 Friday

28 Saturday

29 Sunday

YoDoDeL-Ay-Ee-Oooo

His singing was something between that of a **rat drowning**, a lavatory **flushing** and a **hyena** devouring her **afterbirth** in the Appalachian **Mountains** under a **full moon.**
Evelyn Waugh

September October 2013

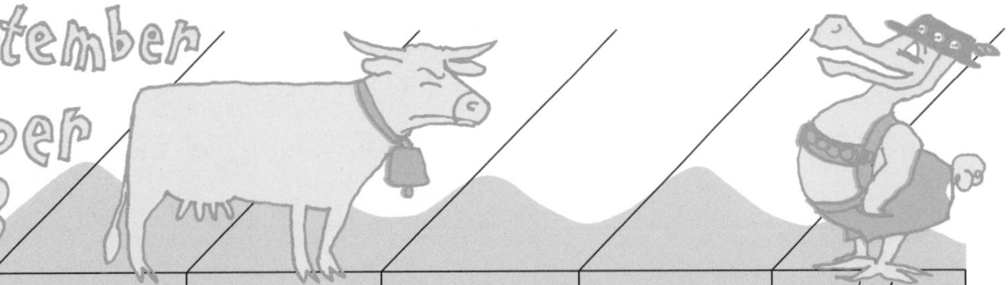

Week 40

30 Monday

1 Tuesday

2 Wednesday

3 Thursday

4 Friday

5 Saturday

6 Sunday

1979 Errol Bird performed the world's longest yodel - 10 hours 15mins

I'm a dyslexic satanist. I worship the drivel.

Linda Smith

October
2013

7 Monday

LabourDay AUS

8 Tuesday

9 Wednesday

10 Thursday

11 Friday

12 Saturday

1875 Birth of Aleister Crowley, satanist & author

13 Sunday

We couldn't afford a proper bath. We just had a pan of water and we'd wash down as far as possible and up as far as possible. Then, when the room was clear, we'd wash possible. *Dolly Parton*

October 2013

14 Monday — Columbus Day US   Thanksgiving   CAN

15 Tuesday — Eid-al-Adha.

16 Wednesday

17 Thursday — 1854 Birth of David Buick, inventor of method of enamelling cast-iron baths

18 Friday

19 Saturday

20 Sunday

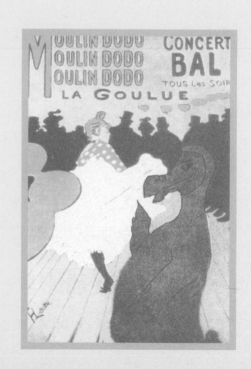

October 2013

21 Monday

22 Tuesday

23 Wednesday

24 Thursday

25 Friday

26 Saturday

27 Sunday

Week 43

1858 Offenbach's 'Orpheus in the Underworld' first performed in Paris. Act 2 contains the Infernal Gallop, better known as the Can-can Music!

BST ends

Lord Dodo has graciously agreed to leave this page free for you to make a start on your Christmas lists.......

...BUT DON'T Be AGHAST AT THe THOUGHT OF WHAT TO BUY!...
VISIT www.dodopad.com FOR LOTS OF CHRISTMAS PRESENT IDEAS

Week 44

Monday Holiday IRE		Labour Day NZ		
Tuesday				
Wednesday				
THURSDAY Hallowe'en				
Friday				
Saturday				
Sunday				●

I'm aghast! - if such a thing exists. *Dick Vosburgh*

When our organs have been transplanted
And the new ones made happy to lodge in us,
Let us pray one wish be granted -
We retain our zones erogenous.

E.Y. Harburg

My ♥ is
dodgy

November 2013

4 Monday

5 Tuesday

6 Wednesday

7 Thursday

8 Friday

9 Saturday

10 Sunday

1922 Birth of Christiaan Barnard, who carried out the world's first human-to-human heart transplant

Have I got moos for you!

Feudalism:
You have
two cows.
The lord of
the manor
takes
some of
the milk.
And all
the
cream.

Totalitarianism:
You have two
cows. The
government
takes them
and denies
they ever
existed.
Milk is
banned.

Fascism:
You have
two cows.
The
government
takes both,
hires you to
take care of
them, and
sells you the
milk.

Democracy:
You have
two cows.
Your
neighbours
pick
someone
to tell you
who gets
the milk.

Political
Correctness:
You are
associated with
(the concept
of "ownership"
is an outdated
symbol of your
decadent,
warmongering,
intolerant past)
two differently-
aged (but no
less valuable to
society) bovines
of non-specified
gender. They
get married and
adopt a calf.

SURREALISM: You have two giraffes. The government requires you to take harmonica lessons.

november 2013

Week 46

Monday — Veterans Day US   Remembrance Day CAN

2 Tuesday

3 Wednesday — Traditional Bull-Running Festival, Stamford, Lincs

4 Thursday

5 Friday

6 Saturday

7 Sunday

Erratum: In my article on the price of milk, "horses" should have read "cows" throughout.

J.C.Morton 'Beachcomber'

November 2013

18 Monday
19 Tuesday
20 Wednesday
21 Thursday
22 Friday
23 Saturday
24 Sunday

Week 47

1835 Patenting of a machine to make horseshoes by Henry Burden of New York

.....Neighbours

NOVEMBER DECEMBER 2013

25 Monday

26 Tuesday

27 Wednesday

28 Thursday — Thanksgiving US   Hanukkah

29 Friday

30 Saturday — St Andrew's Day

Sunday — 1895 Birth of Henry Williamson, author of 'Tarka the Otter'

The Dodo family has always dabbled in garden design, as the fine parterres and herbaceous borders at Dodo Towers bear witness. On a visit in the 1920's to Mount Stewart, County Down, grandfather Dodo was happy to be able to give some words of advice to Lady Londonderry as she planned her exquisite and idiosyncratic gardens. He suggested a monument to the family connection - the renowned Dodo Terrace, with its dodistinctive statues, fashioned by a bemused local stonemason. Immortality was thus assured, and these gardens are now one of the premier jewels in the National Trust's crown.

not entirely dodubious information........

Dodecember 2013

2 Monday

3 Tuesday

4 Wednesday

5 Thursday

6 Friday

7 Saturday

8 Sunday

1878 Birth of Edith Vane-Tempest-Stewart, Marchioness of London-derry, creator of the Mount Stewart Gardens and the Dodo Terrace

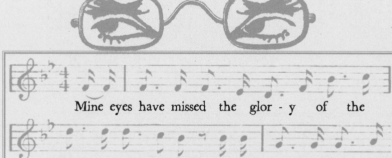

Mine eyes have missed the glor - y of the com- ing of the Lord. By search- ing through my pock- ets where my opt - ic aids are stored.......*H.F. Ellis*

9
MONDAY

10
TUESDAY

11
WEDNESDAY

12
THURSDAY

13
FRIDAY

14
SATURDAY

15
SUNDAY

Week 50

1859 Death of Dr Ludwig Lazarus Zamenhof, oculist and creator of Esperanto

I can speak Esperanto like a native *Spike Milligan*

IT'S A JUNGLE OUT THERE - *HAVE YOU GOT NEXT YEAR'S DODO PAD YET?*
NO TIME TO LOSE!

DECEMBER 2013

16 Monday

17 Tuesday

18 Wednesday

19 Thursday

20 Friday

21 Saturday

22 Sunday

Week 51

○

1956 Birth of Colo at Columbus Zoo, Ohio, the first gorilla to be born in captivity

When astronomers showed Earth was lowly,
Not Heaven's sweet center most holy,
Philosophers grumbled
At theories crumbled.
As one said, "I wish someone had Ptolemy."

December 2013

23 Monday

24 Tuesday

25 Wednesday

26 Thursday

27 Friday

28 Saturday

29 Sunday

Week 52

Christmas Day

Boxing Day UK, AUS, NZ   St Stephen's Day IRE

1571 Birth of astronomer Johannes Kepler

Lord Dodo continues tirelessly with his magnum opus, a lexicon for the 21st century. Just as the last pages of the 2013 edition were going off to the typing pool, he came across these morsels which he felt duty-bound to include....

Gelatine -a device for cutting the heads off jelly babies

Perversion - the cat's side of the story

Eyeliner - a large ship created by Apple Inc.

Cardiology - the study of knitware

Caustic - good heavens, a twig!

He will be delighted to consider any suggestions from readers for the next edition and offers the usual reward for any that make it into print...

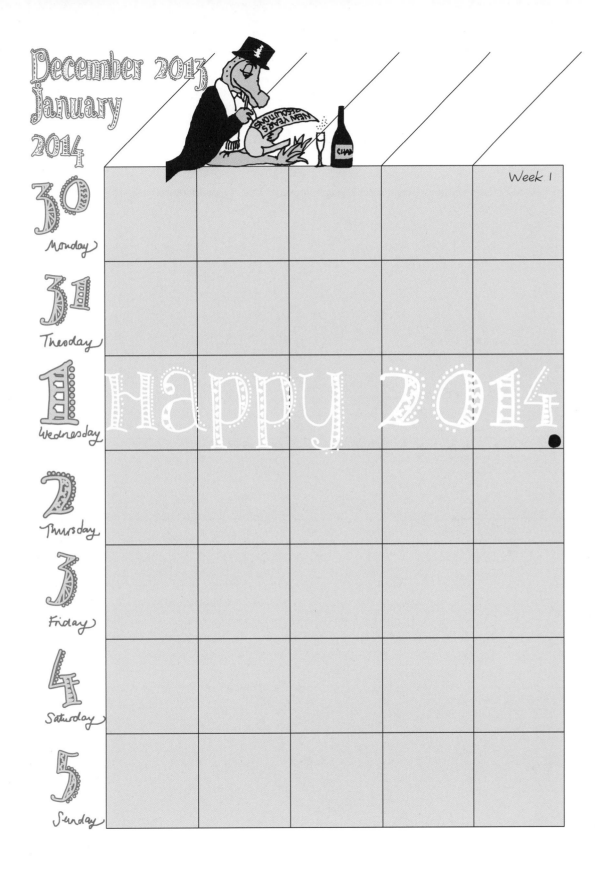

December 2013
January
2014

30 Monday

31 Tuesday

1 Wednesday

2 Thursday

3 Friday

4 Saturday

5 Sunday

Week 1

happy 2014

January 2014

February 2014

March 2014

April 2014

May 2014

June 2014

FORWARD PLANNER 2014

JANUARY 2014

Day		Note	Day		Note
1	W	NEW YEAR'S DAY	17	F	
2	Th	BANK HOLIDAY (SCOT)	18	S	
3	F		19	Su	
4	S		20	M	MARTIN LUTHER KING DAY (US)
5	Su		21	T	
6	M		22	W	
7	T		23	Th	
8	W		24	F	
9	Th		25	S	BURNS' NIGHT
10	F		26	Su	
11	S		27	M	AUSTRALIA DAY (OBS)
12	Su		28	T	
13	M		29	W	
14	T		30	Th	
15	W		31	F	CHINESE NEW YEAR
16	Th				

FEBRUARY 2014

Day		Note	Day		Note
1	S		17	M	PRESIDENTS' DAY (US)
2	Su		18	T	
3	M		19	W	
4	T		20	Th	
5	W		21	F	
6	Th	WAITANGI DAY (NZ)	22	S	
7	F		23	Su	
8	S		24	M	
9	Su		25	T	
10	M		26	W	
11	T		27	Th	
12	W		28	F	
13	Th				
14	F				
15	S				
16	Su				

Public Holidays et al.
This information is correct at time of going to press. The publishers accept no responsibility for any errors.

MARCH 2014

Day		Note	Day		Note
1	S		17	M	
2	Su		18	T	
3	M		19	W	
4	T	SHROVE TUESDAY	20	Th	
5	W		21	F	
6	Th		22	S	
7	F		23	Su	
8	S		24	M	
9	Su		25	T	
10	M	COMMONWEALTH DAY / CANBERRA DAY (AUS)	26	W	
11	T		27	Th	
12	W		28	F	
13	Th		29	S	
14	F		30	Su	MOTHER'S DAY (UK & EIRE) / BST BEGINS
15	S		31	M	
16	Su				

APRIL 2014

Day		Note	Day		Note
1	T		17	Th	
2	W		18	F	GOOD FRIDAY
3	Th		19	S	
4	F		20	Su	EASTER DAY
5	S		21	M	EASTER MONDAY
6	Su		22	T	
7	M		23	W	
8	T		24	Th	
9	W		25	F	ANZAC DAY (AUS & NZ)
10	Th		26	S	
11	F		27	Su	
12	S		28	M	
13	Su		29	T	
14	M		30	W	
15	T	PASSOVER			
16	W				

MAY 2014

Day		Note	Day		Note
1	Th		17	S	
2	F		18	Su	
3	S		19	M	VICTORIA DAY (CANADA)
4	Su		20	T	
5	M	MAY BANK HOLIDAY (UK & EIRE)	21	W	
6	T		22	Th	
7	W		23	F	
8	Th		24	S	
9	F		25	Su	
10	S		26	M	SPRING BANK HOLIDAY (UK) / MEMORIAL DAY (US)
11	Su	MOTHER'S DAY (US & AUS)	27	T	
12	M		28	W	
13	T		29	Th	
14	W		30	F	
15	Th		31	S	
16	F				

JUNE 2014

Day		Note	Day		Note
1	Su		17	T	
2	M	BANK HOLIDAY (EIRE)	18	W	
3	T		19	Th	
4	W		20	F	
5	Th		21	S	
6	F		22	Su	
7	S		23	M	
8	Su		24	T	
9	M		25	W	
10	T		26	Th	
11	W		27	F	
12	Th		28	S	RAMADAN BEGINS
13	F		29	Su	
14	S		30	M	
15	Su	FATHER'S DAY (UK, US & CAN)			
16	M				

FORWARD PLANNER 2014

JULY 2014

Day	Note	Day	Note
1 T	CANADA DAY	17 Th	
2 W		18 F	
3 Th		19 S	
4 F	INDEPENDENCE DAY (US)	20 Su	
5 S		21 M	
6 Su		22 T	
7 M		23 W	
8 T		24 Th	
9 W		25 F	
10 Th		26 S	
11 F		27 Su	
12 S		28 M	
13 Su		29 T	
14 M	PUBLIC HOLIDAY (N. IRELAND) BASTILLE DAY	30 W	
15 T		31 Th	
16 W			

AUGUST 2014

1 F		17 Su	
2 S		18 M	
3 Su		19 T	
4 M	SUMMER BANK HOLIDAY (SCOTLAND & EIRE)	20 W	
5 T		21 Th	
6 W		22 F	
7 Th		23 S	
8 F		24 Su	
9 S		25 M	SUMMER BANK HOLIDAY (UK)
10 Su		26 T	
11 M		27 W	
12 T		28 Th	
13 W		29 F	
14 Th		30 S	
15 F		31 Su	
16 S			

SEPTEMBER 2014

1 M	LABOR DAY (US & CAN)	17 W	
2 T		18 Th	
3 W		19 F	
4 Th		20 S	
5 F		21 Su	
6 S		22 M	
7 Su	FATHER'S DAY (AUS)	23 T	
8 M		24 W	
9 T		25 Th	ROSH HASHANAH
10 W		26 F	
11 Th		27 S	
12 F		28 Su	
13 S		29 M	
14 Su		30 T	
15 M			
16 T			

OCTOBER 2014

1 W		17 F	
2 Th		18 S	
3 F		19 Su	
4 S	YOM KIPPUR EID AL-ADHA	20 M	
5 Su		21 T	
6 M		22 W	
7 T		23 Th	DIWALI
8 W		24 F	
9 Th		25 S	ISLAMIC NEW YEAR
10 F		26 Su	BST ENDS
11 S		27 M	HOLIDAY (EIRE)
12 Su		28 T	
13 M	COLUMBUS DAY (US) THANKSGIVING (CANADA)	29 W	
14 T		30 Th	
15 W		31 F	HALLOWE'EN
16 Th			

NOVEMBER 2014

1 S		17 M	
2 Su		18 T	
3 M		19 W	
4 T		20 Th	
5 W	GUY FAWKES' NIGHT	21 F	
6 Th		22 S	
7 F		23 Su	
8 S		24 M	
9 Su	REMEMBRANCE SUNDAY (UK)	25 T	
10 M		26 W	
11 T	VETERANS' DAY (US) REMEMBRANCE DAY (CAN)	27 Th	THANKSGIVING (US)
12 W		28 F	
13 Th		29 S	
14 F		30 Su	
15 S			
16 Su			

DECEMBER 2014

Day	Note	Day	Note
1 M		17 W	HANUKKAH
2 T		18 Th	
3 W		19 F	
4 Th		20 S	
5 F		21 Su	
6 S		22 M	
7 Su		23 T	
8 M		24 W	
9 T		25 Th	CHRISTMAS DAY
10 W		26 F	BOXING DAY (UK, AUS, NZ) ST. STEPHEN'S DAY (EIRE)
11 Th		27 S	
12 F		28 Su	
13 S		29 M	
14 Su		30 T	
15 M		31 W	
16 T			

THE APPENDIX

starts here

APPENDIX

APPENDIX